Ramadan:
The Month of Fasting

Maulana Wahiduddin Khan

Goodword

According to Islamic teachings, **Ramadan,** the ninth month of the Hijrah calendar, is the month of fasting. All Muslims everywhere have to fast in this month.

The **Quran** says that fasting was common to all religions: "Believers, Allah has ordered fasting for you, just as He ordered it for those before you, so that evil may never touch you." *(Al-Baqarah, 2:183)*.

The Arabic for fasting is 'saum'. It means not taking any food or drink, which is the spirit of Islamic fasting.

In the month of Ramadan, believers take no food or drink for a fixed period each day, that is, from dawn till sunset.

They eat and drink during the night. This goes for a month.

Looked at simply, fasting means to abstain from food and drink but, in spirit, it includes not doing anything which is bad.

Staying away from food and drink during the day is a sign of being willing to do without things. **Ramadan** is, basically a form of annual training for knowing and doing one's duties all the time.

Being a person who knows and does his duty means doing what is wanted and not doing anything bad.

8

9

Ramadan teaches one how to be such a person.

The month of Ramadan begins with seeing the moon when it first appears.

It is written that when the Prophet Muhammad ﷺ saw the new moon of Ramadan, he said: "O Allah, make this month for us a month of peace and bowing to Your will."

12

This saying of the Prophet is like a vow and the month of Ramadan begins from the taking of this vow. According to the vow, believers must live in peace, that is, never fight. This is the true spirit of the month of Ramadan.

During the month, believers must study the Quran more and more, in prayer and out of prayer.

14

Through the study of the message of the Quran;

we find the teachings of the Quran again,
and we think better according to Quranic
rules.

There is a special prayer, said daily in the month of Ramadan, called tarawih. It is said after the isha prayer during the night.

The faithful make contact with God through the Quran, which is the Book of God.

SAEED GENERAL STORE

16

17

The Prophet of Islam once said that the month of Ramadan was the month of giving to others. Fasting makes believers more aware of hunger.

They realise how bad hunger is, so they begin to give more and more during this month.

To encourage everyone to give to others, the Prophet Muhammad ﷺ said that doing so in the month of Ramadan was rewardable more than in any other month.

Give away
old toys

20

ETIKAF

The last 10 days of the month of Ramadan are the days of *etikaf*, that is, staying strictly away from all other people. Etikaf means sitting in the mosque for a fixed period. This saves one from being disturbed by other things and people. *Etikaf* is a period of thinking deeply, looking inside oneself and trying to make oneself a better person.

Ramadan is much more than fasting.

It is the building up of a culture of doing without things so that our thoughts, speech and deeds are purified.

NEXT 20 KM

The message of Ramadan is: choose carefully between right and wrong.

RAMADAN

NEXT 29 DAYS

Don't allow your desires to rule you, but follow principles.

Give up all bad things forever, just as you gave up food and drink for a month.